Give Me Five! ENGLISH

BASICS
ACTIVITY BOOK 1

S	Hello, friends!	page 2
1	Ready for school!	page 6
2	Happy birthday!	page 16
3	At the circus	page 26
	My project 1: Family	page 36
4	Fantastic food!	page 38
5	Fun on the farm	page 48
6	A day in the park	page 58
	My project 2: Spring	page 68
7	Let's explore my town!	page 70
8	Camping fun!	page 80
9	Day and night	page 90
	My project 3: Holidays	page 100
ABC	Vocabulary practice	page 102
	Cambridge Exams Practice	page 111

My name is _____.

Donna Shaw • Joanne Ramsden
Course consultants: Rocío Gutiérrez Burgos and Mónica Pérez Is

macmillan education

Starter Unit — Hello, friends!

Lesson 1

1 Read and match. Say.

one · two · three · four · five · six · seven · eight · nine · ten

2 Think and complete. Say.

hat

2 two

Lesson 2 **Grammar**

1 Read and circle. Say.

1 It's a banana. 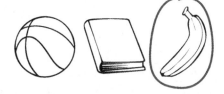   2 It's a sock.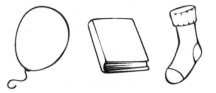

3 It's a square.    4 It's a ball.

5 It's a dog.   6 It's a book.

2 **Talk Partners** Read, trace and circle. Ask and answer.

1 What's this?   2 What's this?   3 What's this?

It's a **ball** / **book**.   It's a **ball** / **hat**.   It's a **book** / **sock**.

dog

three **3**

Lesson 3 Story

After you read

1 Read and colour the bike. Say.

1. What colour is it? It's green and orange!

2. What colour is it? It's blue and yellow!

2 Colour and circle. Ask and answer. **Talk Partners**

What colour is it? It's blue / yellow and green / red.

circle

4 four

Lesson 4 **Vocabulary and Grammar**

1 Listen and point. Say the missing day.

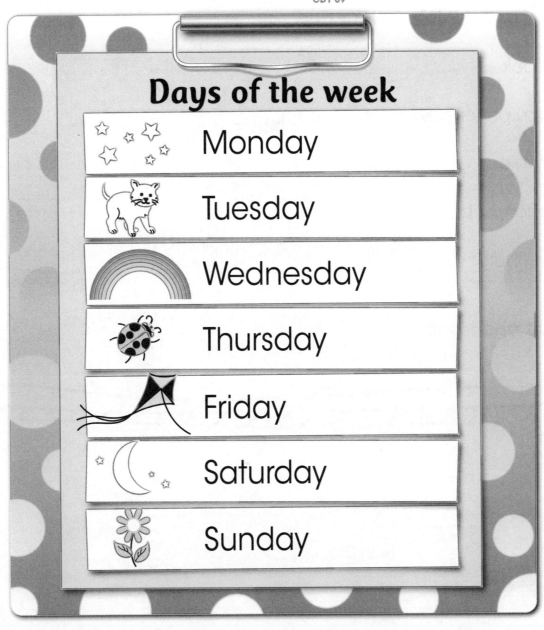

2 💬 **Talk Partners** Read. Ask and answer.

— What day is it today?
— It's Monday.

3  **My progress** Make your traffic light. Listen to the teacher and point.

Key for Activity 3: **1.** I can say the numbers 1-10. **2.** I can say the colours. **3.** I can ask and answer *What day is it today?* **4.** I listen to the teacher. **5.** I listen to other pupils.

  ball

→ Teacher's Resource Bank

five 5

Unit 1 Ready for school!

Lesson 1 **Vocabulary**

1 Read and match. Colour and say.

1 a blue book

2 an orange pencil case

3 a brown ruler

4 a green school bag

5 a red computer

2 Read and trace.

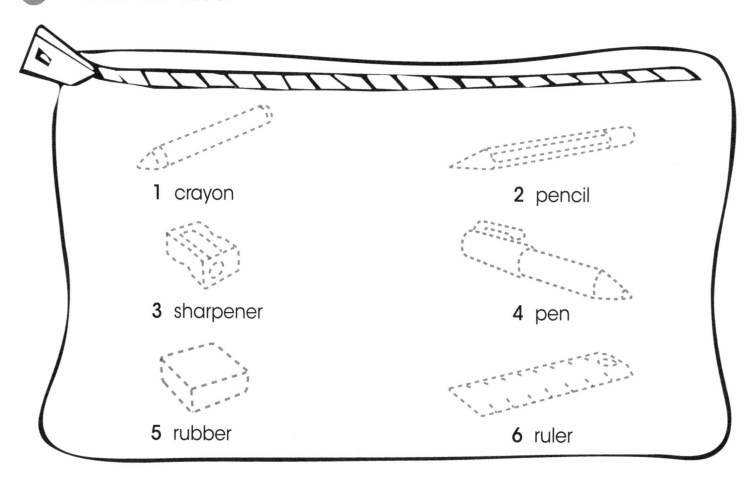

1 crayon

2 pencil

3 sharpener

4 pen

5 rubber

6 ruler

5 five

6 six

Lesson 2 **Grammar**

1 Read, follow and draw.

1 Where's my ruler?

2 Where's my sharpener?

3 Where's my book?

4 Where's my crayon?

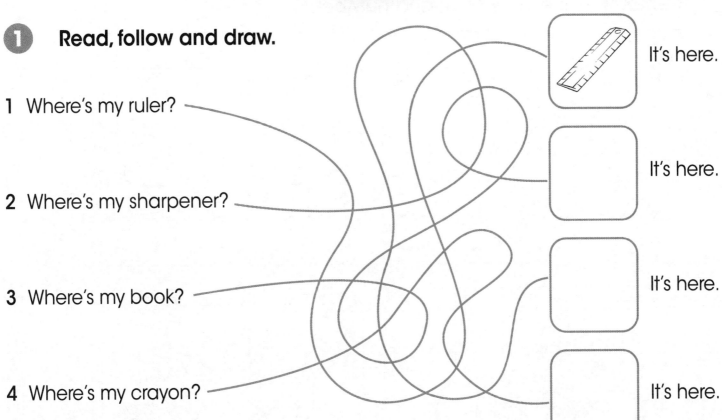

It's here.

It's here.

It's here.

It's here.

2 **Talk Partners** Choose and circle. Act out.

Oh no! Where's my ✏️ 🧽 ?

It's here.

And where's my 📏 🖍 ?

It's here, too. Look!

Thank you.

seven

1 Lesson 3 Story

After you read

1. Remember the story. Look and number.

2. Read. Colour the objects in the story.

1
a black and white book

2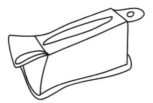
a purple pencil case

3
a pink crayon

 1 One

8 eight

Lesson 4 **Vocabulary and Grammar**

1 Listen and tick (✓).

2 Read and draw.

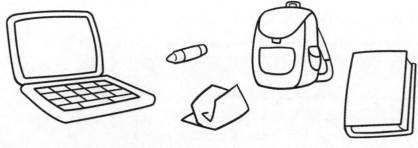

1 Put the book on the shelf.

2 Put the computer on the desk.

3 Put the paper in the bin.

4 Put the school bag under the chair.

5 Put the crayon in the cupboard.

1 Lesson 5 Phonics

1 Say.

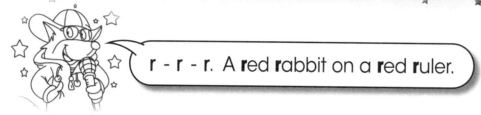

r - r - r. A **r**ed **r**abbit on a **r**ed **r**uler.

Toby's tongue twister

2 Colour the words that begin with 'r'. Say.

rug | ring | pen | rabbit
rat | hat | read | run

3 💬 **Talk Partners** Play *Fast finger!* in pairs.

Rubber!

Here!

Play *Fast finger!*: Pupils play with their Talk Partner. Pupil A says a word and Pupil B points to the picture as quickly as possible. They swap roles and repeat. They continue playing until they have found all the words.

10 ten

Lesson 6 **British culture**

1 Listen and number. Say.

CD1 23

We sing songs.

We listen to the head teacher.

We clap our hands.

We play music.

 Think about your culture

What do you do at school?

2 Read and tick (✓). Draw and say.

1 I listen to the head teacher. ◯

2 I play music. ◯

3 I sit on the floor. ◯

4 I sing songs. ◯

eleven 11

1 Lesson 7 Literacy

After you read

Text type: **A classroom poster**

1 **Read and number.**

1 Listen to others.

2 Put your hand up to speak.

3 Work quietly.

4 Sit down on your chair.

5 Walk in the classroom.

6 Tidy up your things.

2 **Look and colour the good children.**

12 twelve

Lesson 8 Review

1 What's missing? Look, circle and draw.

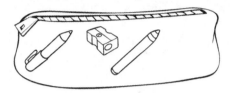 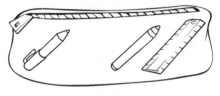

1 Where's my **ruler / crayon**?

2 Where's my **sharpener / pen**?

 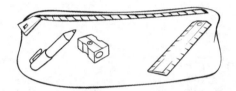

3 Where's my **ruler / pen**?

4 Where's my **crayon / sharpener**?

2 Match and circle.

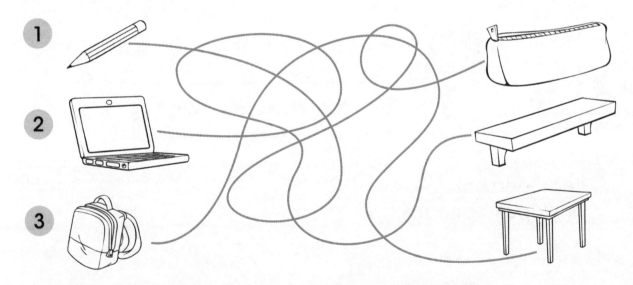

1 Put the **pencil / computer** in the **pencil case / school bag**.

2 Put the **school bag / computer** on the **desk / shelf**.

3 Put the **pencil case / school bag** under the **shelf / desk**.

3 **My progress** Use your traffic light. Listen to the teacher and point.

Key for Activity 3: 1. I can say the names of classroom objects. 2. I can ask *Where's my pen?* 3. I listen to the teacher and my friends. 4. I put my hand up to speak. 5. I tidy up my things.

thirteen

1 Video and 21st Century Skills

Being organised

1 What's missing in the school bag? Listen and circle.

1

2

3

4

What's in your school bag?

2 Read and tick (✓). Draw, point and say.

1 book

2 snack

3 pencil case

4 water

5 ruler

 3 three

14 fourteen

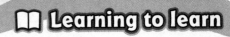

Spelling 1
📖 Learning to learn

Let's practise spelling!

	Look	Read	Trace
1		book	book
2		pen	pen
3		rubber	rubber
4		pencil	pencil
5		ruler	ruler
6		crayon	crayon
7		sharpener	sharpener
8		computer	computer
9		school bag	school bag
10		pencil case	pencil case

 eight

fifteen 15

Unit 2 Happy birthday!

Lesson 1 **Vocabulary**

1 Read, find and colour.

1 a blue ball

2 a red train

3 a brown teddy

4 a green kite

5 a yellow car

6 an orange scooter

2 Read and circle.

16 sixteen

Lesson 2 Grammar

1 **Read, follow and circle.**

1 Is it a doll?
2 Is it a teddy?
3 Is it a ball?
4 Is it a kite?

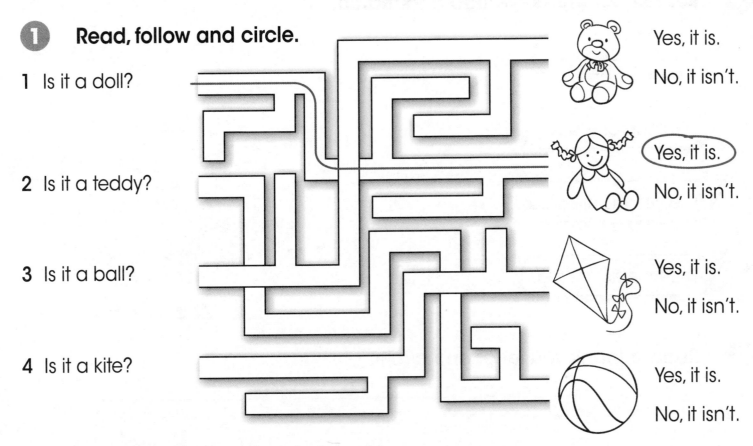

Yes, it is.
No, it isn't.

(Yes, it is.)
No, it isn't.

Yes, it is.
No, it isn't.

Yes, it is.
No, it isn't.

2 **Talk Partners** Choose and circle. Act out.

What is it? Is it a ?

No, it isn't.

Is it a ?

Yes, it is.

It's a fantastic present. Thank you!

ruler

seventeen 17

2 Lesson 3 Story

After you read

1 Remember the story. Read and match.

1. My scooter is fast.
2. My scooter is slow.
3. The wheels are small.
4. The wheels are big.

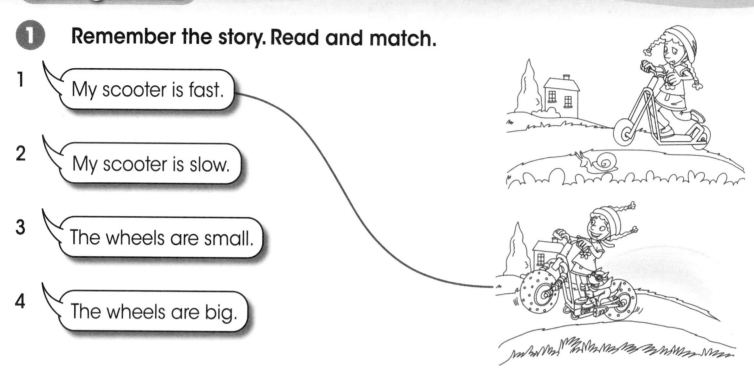

2 Read a thank you letter and circle.

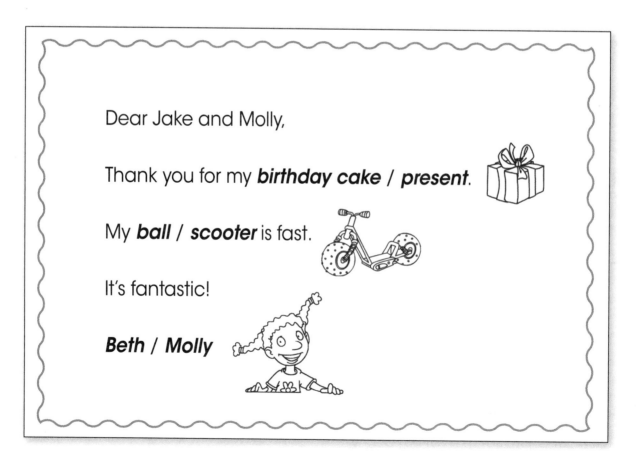

Dear Jake and Molly,

Thank you for my **birthday cake / present**.

My **ball / scooter** is fast.

It's fantastic!

Beth / Molly

rubber

18 eighteen

Lesson 4 **Vocabulary and Grammar** 2

1 Listen and match. CD1 37

2 Read and circle. Draw. Ask and answer. Talk Partners

What's your favourite toy?

My favourite toy is a **ball** / **doll** / **robot**. It's **big** / **small**.

Computer

nineteen 19

2 Lesson 5 Phonics

1 Say.

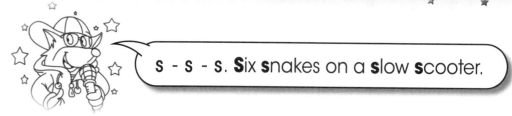

Toby's tongue twister

s - s - s. **S**ix **s**nakes on a **s**low **s**cooter.

2 Colour the words that begin with 's'. Say.

seven — socks — cat — scooter
swim — sing — snail — crayon

3 💬 Talk Partners Play *What's my word?* in pairs.

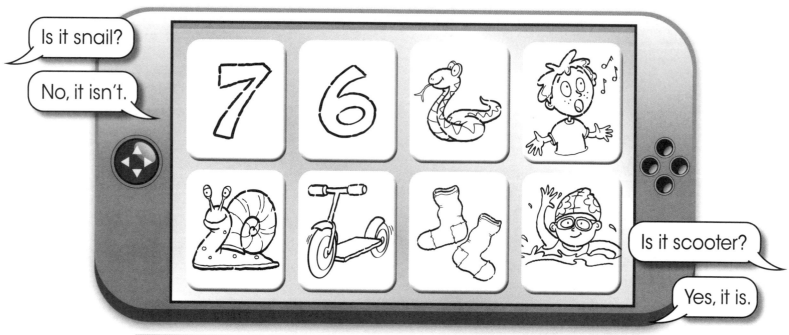

Is it snail?
No, it isn't.
Is it scooter?
Yes, it is.

Play *What's my word?*: Pupils play with their Talk Partner. This is a guessing game. Pupil A chooses a word and Pupil B asks the question *Is it...?* When Pupil B guesses correctly, they swap roles and repeat.

20 twenty

Lesson 6 **British culture**

1 Listen and circle.

1    2

3    4

Think about your culture

What do you do on your birthday?

2 Read and tick (✓). Draw and say.

1 I have presents.

2 I have a birthday cake.

3 I play party games.

4 I wear fancy dress.

 sharpener

twenty-one 21

2 Lesson 7 Literacy

After you read

Text type: **A birthday card**

1 Read again. Choose *yes* or *no*.

1 The birthday card is for Beth.   **yes / no**

2 Beth is eight today.   **yes / no**

3 Beth is seven today.   **yes / no**

4 The birthday card is from Molly and Jake.   **yes / no**

5 The birthday cake has seven candles.   **yes / no**

2 Read. Draw a picture on the birthday card.

The birthday cake has got seven candles.
The present is big.

22 twenty-two

Lesson 8 **Review** 2

1 Look, trace and match.

1

2

3

4

5

6

dinosaur

car

scooter

doll

ball

robot

2 Look, read and circle.

1
It's *big / small*.

2
It's *old / new*.

3
It's *fast / slow*.

4
It's *slow / fast*.

5
It's *old / new*.

6
It's *big / small*.

3 **My progress** Use your traffic light. Listen to the teacher and point.

Key for Activity 3: 1. I can say the names of toys. 2. I can talk about my favourite toy. 3. I can sing songs. 4. I listen to the teacher. 5. I listen to other pupils. 6. I help other pupils.

 book

twenty-three 23

2 Video and 21st Century Skills

Ordering

1 Read and listen. Circle the favourite things.
CD1 46

1 My three favourite toys
1. train / (bike) / scooter
2. ball
3. computer game

2 My three favourite colours
1. blue / purple / pink
2. yellow
3. red

3 My three favourite days
1. Friday / Saturday / Sunday
2. Monday
3. Wednesday

4 My three favourite animals
1. cat / dog / snail
2. rabbit
3. rat

What are your three favourite toys?

2 Think and choose. Draw your number one toy. Say.

This is my favourite toy.

It's **red / blue** and **yellow / purple**.

It's **big / small**.

It's **new / old**.

  pencil case

24 twenty-four

Spelling 2

Learning to learn

Let's practise spelling!

	Look	Read	Trace
1		ball	ball
2		train	train
3		car	car
4		doll	doll
5		kite	kite
6		robot	robot
7		scooter	scooter
8		teddy	teddy
9		dinosaur	dinosaur
10		computer game	computer game

school bag

twenty-five

Unit 3 At the circus

Lesson 1 **Vocabulary**

1 Read and match. Say.

 head

 mouth

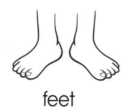 feet

nose

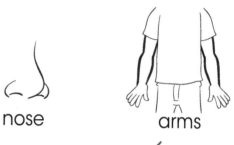 arms

one   two   ten

 ears

 legs

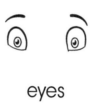 eyes

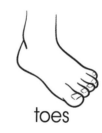 toes

 fingers

2 Count and tick (✓) or cross (✗).

1 four heads

2 ten hands

3 four noses

4 eight eyes

5 seven legs

 Car

26 twenty-six

Lesson 2 **Grammar** 3

1 Read and draw a clown. Colour.

1 I've got a big head.

2 I've got small ears.

3 I've got a big nose.

4 I've got small eyes.

5 I've got a big mouth.

2 Talk Partners Choose and circle. Act out.

Look at me! I've got a big  .

I've got big 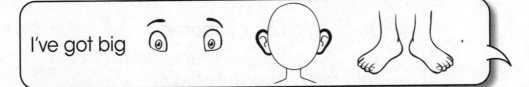 .

I'm a clown.

I'm a clown, too.

twenty-seven 27

3 Lesson 3 Story

After you read

1 Remember the story. Look and number.

2 Read the circus poster. Look and circle.

Come to the **circus** / **park**!

See the fantastic **clown** / **acrobat**.

See amazing Toby.

See the magic **kite** / **scooter**.

See Molly the **acrobat** / **clown**.

It's fantastic!

teddy

28 twenty-eight

Lesson 4 **Vocabulary and Grammar** 3

1 Listen and colour.

2 Draw and colour a friend. Circle and say.

My friend has got *long / short* hair.

My friend has got *green / brown / blue* eyes.

computer games

twenty-nine 29

3 Lesson 5 Phonics

1. Say.

h - h - h. **H**elen the **h**appy hippo **h**ops and **h**ops.

2. Colour the words that begin with 'h'. Say.

hat | hair | arm | horse
hand | happy | eye | head

3. 💬 **Talk Partners** Play *Fast finger!* in pairs.

Happy!

Here!

Play *Fast finger!*: Pupils play with their Talk Partner. Pupil A says a word and Pupil B points to the picture as quickly as possible. They swap roles and repeat. They continue playing until they have found all the words.

30 thirty

Lesson 6 **British culture**

1 Listen and number.
CD2 08

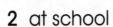 Think about your culture

Where do you paint your face?

2 Read and tick (✓). Draw and say.

1 at a birthday party

2 at school

3 at the circus

4 at home

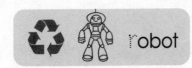 robot

thirty-one **31**

3 Lesson 7 **Literacy**

After you read

 Text type: **An action rhyme**

1 Read and draw the faces.

1  I'm angry.

2  I'm sad.

3  I'm tired.

4 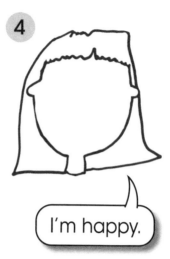 I'm happy.

2 Read the rhyme and match. Say.

My feelings

When I'm sad,
I sit and cry.

When I'm happy,
I laugh and smile.

When I'm angry,
I stamp my feet.

When I'm tired,
I go to sleep.

  ball

32 thirty-two

Lesson 8 Review 3

1 Trace and read about you. Draw.

1 I've got one head.

2 I've got two arms.

3 I've got two legs.

4 I've got two feet.

5 I've got ten fingers.

6 I've got ten toes.

me

2 Read. Choose *yes* or *no*.

1 Molly has got blue eyes.   yes / no

2 Jake has got long hair.   yes / no

3 Beth has got short hair.   yes / no

4 Toby has got black and white hair. yes / no

3 My progress Use your traffic light. Listen to the teacher and point.

Key for Activity 3: 1. I can say the parts of the body.
2. I can talk about my friend's hair and my friend's eyes.
3. I can say an action rhyme. 4. I listen to the teacher.
5. I listen to other pupils. 6. I help other pupils.

dinosaur

thirty-three 33

3 Video and 21st Century Skills

Working together

1 Listen and number.
CD2 13

We play football together. ◯

We play music together. ◯

We tidy up together. ◯

We juggle together. ①

What do you do with your friends?

2 Read and tick (✓). Draw you and your friends.

1 I sing with my friends. ◯

2 I tidy up with my friends. ◯

3 I draw pictures with my friends. ◯

4 I play with my friends. ◯

  scooter

34 thirty-four

Spelling 3
Learning to learn

Let's practise spelling!

	Look	Read	Trace
1		head	head
2		legs	legs
3		feet	feet
4		toes	toes
5		arms	arms
6		ears	ears
7		mouth	mouth
8		eyes	eyes
9		nose	nose
10		fingers	fingers

train

thirty-five

My project 1 Lesson 1

Plan your project

 1 Plan your family leaf.

1 Read and colour.

orange   light green   dark green   red   yellow   brown

2 Who is in your family leaf? Read and tick (✓).

my mother ◯   my uncle ◯

my father ◯   my cousin ◯

my sister ◯   my grandmother ◯

my brother ◯   my grandfather ◯

my aunt ◯

3 What is the title of your leaf? Choose and circle.

This is my **big** / **small** / **fantastic** / **happy** family!

36 thirty-six

My project 1 Lesson 2

1. Read and circle.

1. This is my mother.
   His / Her name is Anna.

2. This is my father.
   His / Her name is Tom.

3. This is my sister.
   His / Her name is Sue.

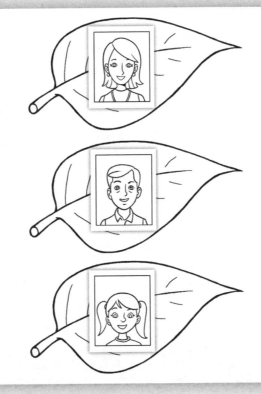

Think about your project

2. Read, think and colour the stars.

I listen to my friends.

I share my things.

I help my friends.

I make an effort.

I like the family leaf.

thirty-seven 37

Unit 4 Fantastic food!

Lesson 1 **Vocabulary**

1 Read and match.

1. eggs and rice
2. chicken and chips
3. salad and meat

2 Trace. Read and match.

1 I've got rice and fish.

2 I've got cake and ice cream.

3 I've got salad and fruit.

two eyes

38 thirty-eight

Lesson 2 Grammar 4

1 Read. Look and match.

1 I like chicken.

2 I don't like meat.

3 I like cake.

4 I love chips.

5 I don't like rice.

6 I like fruit.

2 Talk Partners Choose and circle. Act out.

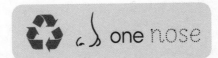

thirty-nine 39

4 Lesson 3 **Story**

After you read

1 Remember the story. Read, look and match.

I don't like oranges.
I don't like peaches.

I like ice cream.

I like cake.

2 What about you? Draw the food.

I like   I love   I don't like

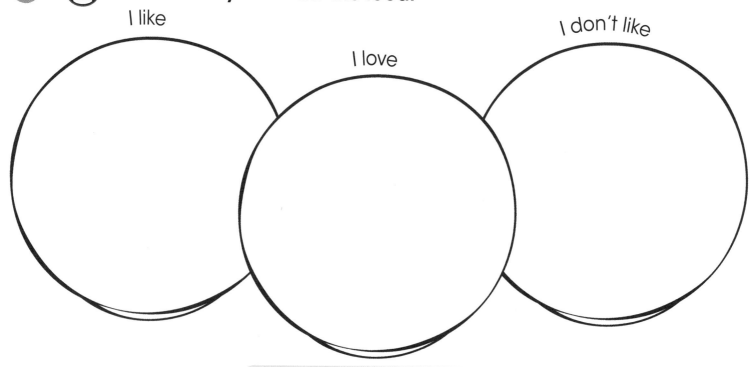

five fingers

40 forty

Lesson 4 **Vocabulary and Grammar**

1 Listen and tick (✓) or cross (✗).

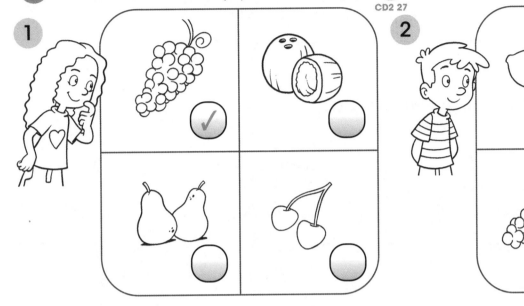

2 Look and circle.

1 Do you like mangoes?   Yes, I do.   No, I don't.

2 Do you like lemons?   Yes, I do.   No, I don't.

3 Do you like peaches?   Yes, I do.   No, I don't.

4 Do you like grapes?   Yes, I do.   No, I don't.

5 Do you like cherries?   Yes, I do.   No, I don't.

6 Do you like coconut?   Yes, I do.   No, I don't.

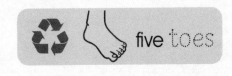

five toes

forty-one

4 Lesson 5 Phonics

1 Write and say.

Toby's tongue twister

j – j – j. Jim juggles jam, juice and jelly.

2 Colour the words that begin with 'j'. Say.

jeans   cherries   jacket   jug

jump   jam   girl   juggle

3 💬 **Talk Partners** Play *What's my word?* in pairs.

Is it *jump*?

No, it isn't.

Is it *jelly*?

Yes, it is.

Play *What's my word?*: Pupils play with their Talk Partner. This is a guessing game. Pupil A chooses a word and Pupil B asks the question *Is it...?* When Pupil B guesses correctly, they swap roles and repeat.

two legs

42 forty-two

Lesson 6 **British culture**

1 Listen and number. Circle the breakfast you like.
CD2 32

What do you have for breakfast?

2 Read and tick (✓). Draw.

1 I have eggs.

2 I have cereal.

3 I have orange juice.

4 I have bread.

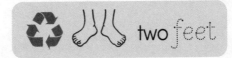

forty-three 43

4 Lesson 7 **Literacy**

 Text type: **A lunch menu**

After you read

1 Read again. Tick (✓) or cross (✗).

1 We've got on Monday. ____

2 We've got on Friday. ____ ◯

3 We've got on Friday. ____ ◯

4 We've got on Monday ____ and Thursday. ____

5 We've got on Wednesday ____ and Friday. ____

What's for lunch on Monday?

2 Draw a lunch menu. Say.

Munch! Munch! Munch! Is this a healthy lunch?

Day: Wednesday

two ears

44 forty-four

Lesson 8 Review 4

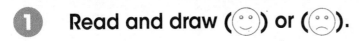

1 Read and draw (☺) or (☹).

1  I don't like fish.
I like fruit salad and eggs.
I love soup.

2  I don't like rice.
I like chips and meat.
I love ice cream.

2 Trace. Ask and answer. Tick (✓) or cross (✗). 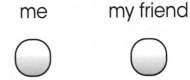 Talk Partners

		me	my friend
1	 Do you like cherries?	◯	◯
2	 Do you like coconuts?	◯	◯
3	Do you like grapes?	◯	◯
4	 Do you like mangoes?	◯	◯

3 **My progress** Use your traffic light. Listen to the teacher and point.

Key for Activity 3: 1. I can say the food words.
2. I can talk about food I like and don't like.
3. I can write a lunch menu. 4. I listen to the teacher.
5. I help other pupils. 6. I work quietly in class.

 one mouth

forty-five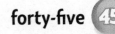

4 Video and 21st Century Skills

Healthy eating

1 Listen and number.

What healthy food do you like?

2 Think and circle. Draw your healthy food in the lunch box.

In my lunch box, I've got
fruit / cereal / bread / orange juice.

I love *grapes / mangoes / cherries*.

two arms

46 forty-six

Spelling 4

Learning to learn

Let's practise spelling!

	Look	Trace	Copy
1		meat	___eat
2		eggs	___ggs
3		fish	___ish
4		chips	___hips
5		rice	___ice
6		cake	___ake
7		salad	___alad
8		chicken	___hicken
9		fruit	___ruit
10		ice cream	___ce ___ream

one head

forty-seven

Fun on the farm

Lesson 1 Vocabulary

1 **Read, find and colour. Point and say.**

Here's the goat. It's brown.

1 Colour the goat brown.

2 Colour the frog green.

3 Colour the cat grey.

4 Colour the chicken orange.

5 Colour the sheep black.

2 **Trace and match.**

1
2
3

cow

mouse

chicken

bird

horse

duck

4
5
6

fish

48 forty-eight

Lesson 2 **Grammar** 5

1 **Read, follow and circle.**

1 Can you see a goat?

2 Can you see a duck?

3 Can you see a sheep?

4 Can you see a frog?

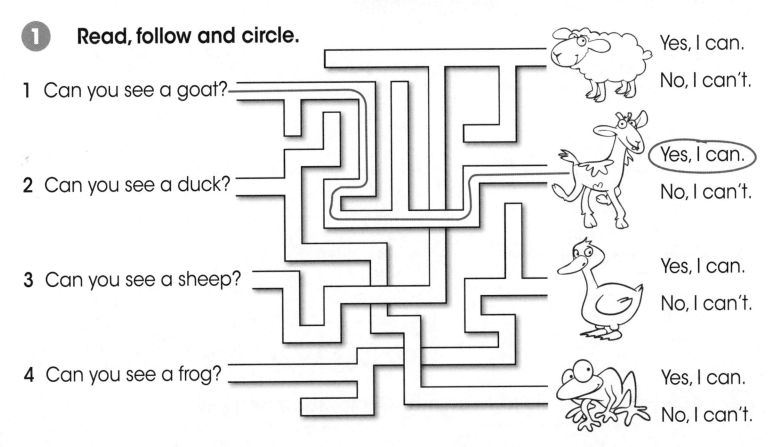

2 💬 **Talk Partners** Read a conversation. Draw an animal. Act out.

forty-nine 49

5 Lesson 3 **Story**

After you read

1 Remember the story. Read and match.

1 Dogs can't climb trees.

2 But goats can't swim.

3 Look at the sheep!

4 Look. Is it a cow?

2 Draw a magic farm animal. Circle, trace and say.

fly

swim

climb

My magic animal can fly / swim / climb.

chicken

50 fifty

Lesson 4 **Vocabulary and Grammar**

1 What do you think? Read and circle. Listen and check.

(Cats can climb trees.)
Cats can't climb trees.

Goats can climb trees.
Goats can't climb trees.

Horses can swim.
Horses can't swim.

Ducks can fly.
Ducks can't fly.

2 Trace and match.

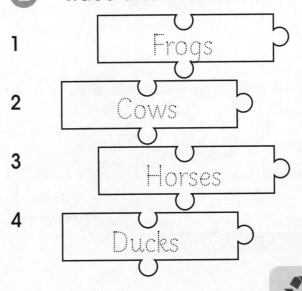

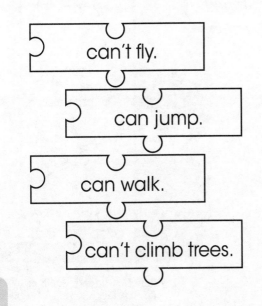

1 Frogs — can't fly.
2 Cows — can jump.
3 Horses — can walk.
4 Ducks — can't climb trees.

fruit

5 Lesson 5 Phonics

1 Trace and say.

Toby's tongue twister

sh – sh – sh. Shush! Don't shout, sheep!

2 Colour the words that begin with 'sh'. Say.

| sharpener | shell | short | sandwich |
| shelf | socks | shop | shark |

3 💬 Talk Partners Play *Fast finger!* in pairs.

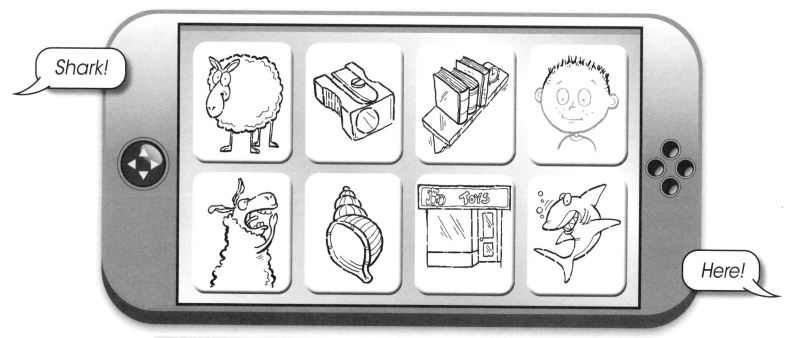

Shark!

Here!

Play *Fast finger!*: Pupils play with their Talk Partner. Pupil A says a word and Pupil B points to the picture as quickly as possible. They swap roles and repeat. They continue playing until they have found all the words.

cake

52 fifty-two

Lesson 6 **British culture**

1 Listen and number.
CD2 51

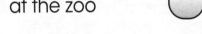 Think about your culture

Where can you see animals in your town?

2 Read and tick (✓). Draw and circle.

1 at the zoo

2 in the park

3 at the pet shop

4 on a farm

I can see **a goat** / **a duck** / **a cat** / **a mouse** / **a frog**.

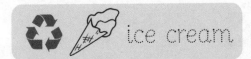

fifty-three 53

5 Lesson 7 **Literacy**

After you read

 Text type: **Animal riddles**

1 Read and trace. Circle and colour the animal.

1
I've got two legs.

I can swim.

I can fly.

I'm small.

I'm brown.

What am I?

2
I've got four legs.

I can walk.

I can't climb.

I'm big.

I'm black and white.

What am I?

2 Choose and say an animal riddle.

 **What am I?**

I've got **two / four** legs.

I can **fly / run / swim**. I can't **fly / climb / jump**.

I'm **brown / green / yellow / black and white**.

 Answer:

I'm a **dog / horse / bird / frog**.

 meat

54 fifty-four

Lesson 8 Review   5

1   Read and count. Circle *Yes, I can* or *No, I can't*.

1 Can you see two cows?
   Yes, I can. / *No, I can't.*

2 Can you see six chickens?
   Yes, I can. / *No, I can't.*

3 Can you see three goats?
   Yes, I can. / *No, I can't.*

4 Can you see two frogs?
   Yes, I can. / *No, I can't.*

5 Can you see a cat?
   Yes, I can. / *No, I can't.*

2   Look, follow and trace.

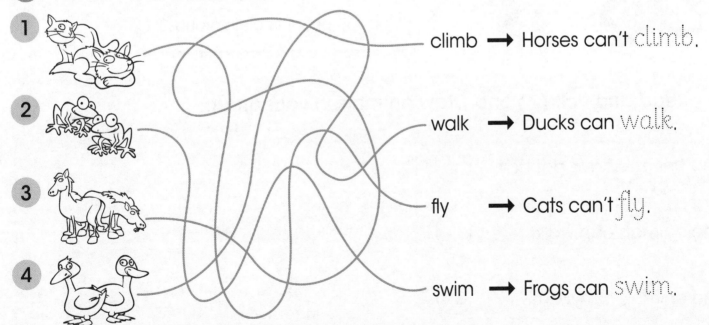

1   climb → Horses can't climb.
2   walk → Ducks can walk.
3   fly → Cats can't fly.
4   swim → Frogs can swim.

3   **My progress**   Use your traffic light. Listen to the teacher and point.

<u>Key for Activity 3:</u> **1.** I can say the animal words. **2.** I can say what animals can do. **3.** I can say what I can see. **4.** I can write a riddle **5.** I listen to the teacher. **6.** I take turns.

fifty-five 55

Grouping

1 Listen and number.
CD2 55

Can you put animals in groups?

2 Read and tick (✓) one. Draw animals in your group.

1 The animals have got hair. ◯

2 The animals can walk. ◯

3 The animals can swim. ◯

4 The animals eat meat. ◯

56 fifty-six

Spelling 5

Learning to learn

Let's practise spelling!

	Look	Trace	Copy
1		mouse	___ouse
2		cat	___at
3		frog	___rog
4		cow	___ow
5		sheep	___heep
6		duck	___uck
7		goat	___oat
8		bird	___ird
9		horse	___orse
10		chicken	___hicken

chips

fifty-seven 57

Unit 6 A day in the park

Lesson 1 Vocabulary

1 Read and look. Tick (✓) or cross (✗).

1 I can see grass in the park.

2 I can see six bushes in the park.

3 I can see a big tree in the park.

4 I can see two flowers in the park.

5 I can see three rocks in the park.

2 Trace. Colour the objects you like.

1 slide

2 seesaw

3 climbing frame

4 swing

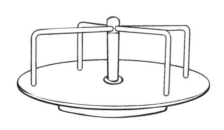

5 roundabout

♻ 🐭 mouse

58 fifty-eight

Lesson 2 Grammar 6

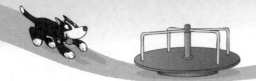

1 Read, follow and trace.

1 Where's Toby? — She's on the seesaw.
2 Where's Molly? — He's on the rock.
3 Where's Beth? — He is on the swing.
4 Where's Jake? — She is on the roundabout.

2 💬 **Talk Partners** Choose and circle. Act out.

Where's [ ] [ ] ?

She's on the [ ] [ ] [ ] . Look!

And where's [ ] [ ] ?

They are on the [ ] [ ] .
Come on. Let's play, too.

duck

fifty-nine 59

6 Lesson 3 Story

After you read

1 Remember the story. Read and tick (✓).

1 What game do the children play?

football

hide and seek ✓

tennis

2 Where are Jake and Molly?

behind a tree

behind a bush

in the long grass

3 What can Toby do?

go in the playground

have a ride on the magic bike

play hide and seek

2 Look at the story again. Read and match.

1 Sorry, Toby. You can't play in here.

2 Ready or not, here I come!

3 They're behind the tree.

4 You can have a ride on the magic bike.

chicken

Lesson 4 **Vocabulary and Grammar** 6

1 Listen and tick (✓).
CD3 10

2 Read and look. Circle and trace.

1 Where are the big dogs?

They're between / behind the trees.

2 Where are the dogs with long hair?

They're next to / behind the bush.

3 Where are the small dogs?

They're between / next to the flowers.

4 Where are the long dogs?

They're behind / in front of the rocks.

horse

sixty-one 61

6 Lesson 5 Phonics

1 Trace and say.

w – w – w. Wally the worm washes windows.

2 Colour the words that begin with 'w'. Say.

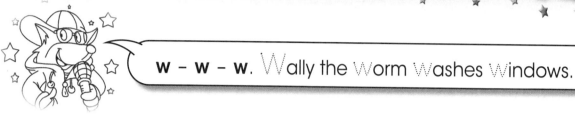

| walk | water | goat | Wednesday |
| week | wall | weather | ruler |

3 💬 **Talk Partners** Play *What's my word?* in pairs.

Is it *window*?

No, it isn't.

Is it *worm*?

Yes, it is.

Play *What's my word?*: Pupils play with their Talk Partner. This is a guessing game. Pupil A chooses a word and Pupil B asks the question *Is it...?* When Pupil B guesses correctly, they swap roles and repeat.

♻ sheep

Lesson 6 **British culture**

1 Listen and match. CD3 15

1 Ann
2 Tom
3 Bill
4 Tony and Alex

Think about your culture

What do you do at the park?

2 Read and tick (✓). Draw.

1 I play in the playground.
2 I have a picnic.
3 I play football on the grass.
4 I feed the ducks.

goat

sixty-three 63

Lesson 7 **Literacy**

After you read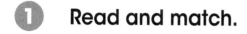

Text type: **Instructions**

1 **Read and match.**

1 Put the soil in a pot.

2 Push the seeds into the soil with your finger.

3 Water the seeds.

4 Put the pot in a sunny place. Watch the plants grow.

5 Put the plants in the garden. Watch the flowers grow.

2 **Order the instructions. Draw.**

1

Water the seeds.

2

Put the pot in a sunny place.

3

Push the seeds into the soil.

 frog

64 sixty-four

Lesson 8 Review 6

1 Read, match and trace.

1 Where's Molly? — She's on the roundabout.

2 Where's Jake? — He's on the swing.

3 Where are Molly and Beth? — They're on the seesaw.

4 Where's Beth? — She's on the slide.

2 Read, look and choose yes or no.

1 The frogs are next to the rocks.   yes / no

2 Molly is in front of the bush.   yes / no

3 The cats are behind the flowers.   yes / no

4 Beth is near the tree.   yes / no

5 Jake is between two rocks.   yes / no

3   My progress   Use your traffic light. Listen to the teacher and point.

Key for Activity 3: 1. I can say the objects in the park. 2. I can say where people and things are. 3. I can talk about a park in my town. 4. I can understand instructions. 5. I listen to instructions in the classroom. 6. I listen to others.

sixty-five 65

6 Video and 21st Century Skills

Being careful

1 Read, listen and match.

1  I use two hands on the
2  I wait next to
3 I sit down on
4  I go down

21 CHANNEL → Are you careful in the playground? What do you do?

2 Read and think. Draw and say.

1 I use two hands on the .
2 I go down the .
3 I sit down on the .
4 I wait next to the 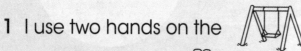 .

 bird

66 sixty-six

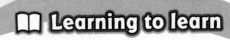

Spelling 6

Learning to learn

Let's practise spelling!

	Look	Trace	Copy
1		swing	_____
2		slide	_____
3		seesaw	_____
4		roundabout	_____
5		climbing frame	_____
6		grass	_____
7		flower	_____
8		tree	_____
9		bush	_____
10		rock	_____

cat

sixty-seven 67

My project 2 Lesson 1

Plan your project

 Plan a spring wall display. Decide with your class and tick (✓).

1 What's the weather like on your wall display?

It's sunny. ◯   It's rainy. ◯

It's windy. ◯   It's cloudy. ◯

2 What animals are on your wall display?

lambs ◯   butterflies ◯

birds ◯   chicks ◯

rabbits ◯

3 What other things are on your wall display?

trees ◯   flowers ◯

grass ◯   bushes ◯

4 What is the title of your wall display?

Spring is here! ◯   It's spring! ◯

Our spring garden ◯   We love spring! ◯

My project 2 Lesson 2

1 Look at your wall display. Circle.

1 The weather is **sunny** / **rainy** / **cloudy** / **windy**.

2 The weather isn't **sunny** / **rainy** / **cloudy** / **windy**.

3 I can see **butterflies** / **rabbits** / **birds and flowers** / **trees** / **grass**.

4 My favourite spring animal is a **rabbit** / **lamb** / **bird** / **chick**.

Think about your project

 Read, think and colour the stars.

I listen to my friends.

I share my things.

I help my friends.

I make an effort.

I like the display.

sixty-nine 69

Unit 7 Let's explore my town!

Lesson 1 Vocabulary

1 Read and match. Point and say.

1 Let's go to the café.
2 Let's go to the bookshop.
3 Let's go to the sweet shop.
4 Let's go to the toyshop.
5 Let's go to the supermarket.
6 Let's go to the cinema.

2 Look and write.

zoo   café   hospital   restaurant   swimming pool   supermarket

1 _hospital_
2 _____
3 _____
4 _____
5 _____
6 _____

f_____

70 seventy

Lesson 2 Grammar 7

1 Count and write.

~~cafés~~ cinema ~~supermarket~~ sweet shops toyshops hospital

1 There's a ____supermarket____.
2 There are ____two cafés____.
3 There's a _____.
4 There are _____.
5 _____.
6 _____.

2  Write about your town. Draw.

1 There's a _____.
2 There are _____.
3 There _____.
4 There _____.

t_____

seventy-one 71

7 Lesson 3 Story

After you read

1 Remember the story. Read and circle *true* or *false*.

1 There's an old tree on the treasure map. (true) false
2 The old tree is behind the swimming pool. true false
3 There are two yellow rocks on the treasure map. true false
4 The yellow rocks are near the zoo. true false
5 The treasure is next to a bush. true false

2 Draw a treasure map. Hide your treasure. Write.

There's a __house_____.

There _____.

There _____.

The treasure is _____.

b_____

Lesson 4 **Vocabulary and Grammar** 7

1 Listen and join the numbers. What is it?

CD3 33

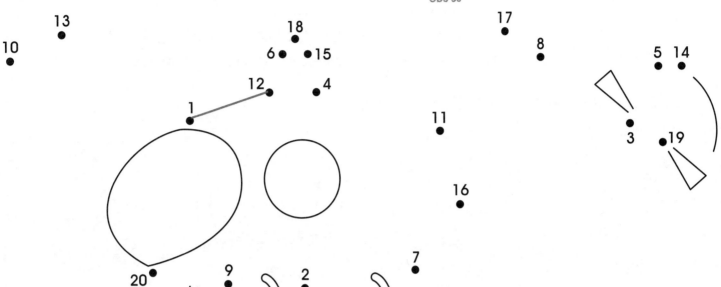

It's a _____.

2 Look, think and write.

eighteen   ~~twelve~~   fourteen   twenty   fifteen   thirteen   sixteen

1   eleven   twelve   _____   fourteen

2   seventeen   _____   nineteen   _____

3   thirteen   _____   _____   _____

g_____

seventy-three 73

7 Lesson 5 Phonics

1 Write and say.

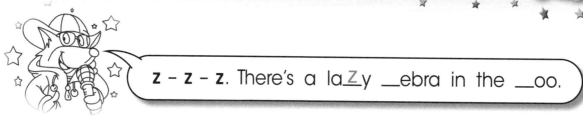

z – z – z. There's a la_z_y __ebra in the __oo.

Toby's tongue twister

2 Colour the words that have 'z'. Say.

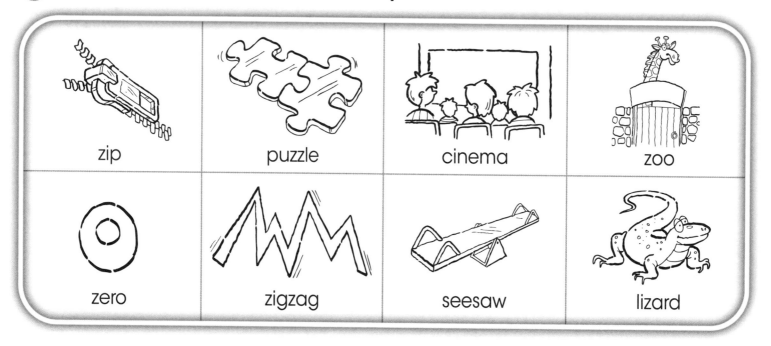

| zip | puzzle | cinema | zoo |
| zero | zigzag | seesaw | lizard |

3 💬 **Talk Partners** Play *Fast finger!* in pairs.

Lazy!

Here!

Play Fast finger!: Pupils play with their Talk Partner. Pupil A says a word and Pupil B points to the picture as quickly as possible. They swap roles and repeat. They continue playing until they have found all the words.

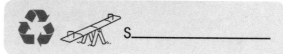

s_____

74 seventy-four

Lesson 6 British culture

1 Listen and number. Draw the line. CD3 37

Think about your culture

How do you travel in your town?

2 Read and tick (✓). Draw, write and say.

1 I travel by boat.
2 I travel by train.
3 I travel by bus.
4 I travel by car.
5 I travel by bike.

I _____.

S _____.

seventy-five 75

7 Lesson 7 **Literacy**

After you read

 Text type: **A fable**

1 Read again and write.

ice cream   apples   ~~countryside~~   cheese   cats   town   cake   apples

I live in the __countryside__.

I eat _____ and _____.

I don't like _____.

I live in the _____.

I eat _____ and _____.

I don't like _____.

2 What do we learn from the fable? Read and circle.

There are **good / bad** things where you live.

3  Read and write. Draw.

What do you like in your town?

I like the _____

_____.

 s_____

 seventy-six

Lesson 8 Review 7

1 Look and write.

1 There's a _sweet shop_ in the town.   2 There's a _____.

3 _____.   4 _____.

5 _____.   6 _____.

2 Count and write.

1 There are __sixteen__ wheels.   2 There are _____ wheels.

3 _____ wheels.   4 _____ wheels.

3   **My progress** Use your traffic light. Listen to the teacher and point.

Key for Activity 3: 1. I can say the places in the town. 2. I can count to twenty. 3. I can say different types of transport. 4. I can read a fable. 5. I listen to the teacher. 6. I help other pupils.

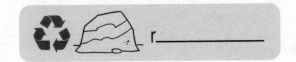

seventy-seven 77

7 Video and 21st Century Skills

Reading digital maps

1 Listen and number the places on the digital map. *CD3 41*

 What places are near your house?

2 Read, think and write. Draw a map. Say.

1 There is _____ near my house.

2 There _____ _____.

3 _____ _____.

  c_____ f_____

78 seventy-eight

Spelling 7

Learning to learn

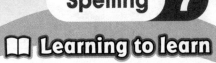

Let's practise spelling!

	Look	Copy	Cover and write
1	zoo	_____	_____
2	café	_____	_____
3	sweet shop	_____	_____
4	toyshop	_____	_____
5	bookshop	_____	_____
6	hospital	_____	_____
7	restaurant	_____	_____
8	swimming pool	_____	_____
9	cinema	_____	_____
10	supermarket	_____	_____

r_____

seventy-nine 79

Unit 8 Camping fun!

Lesson 1 **Vocabulary**

1 Read, match and colour.

1 a green shirt
2 grey shorts
3 red trainers
4 brown shoes
5 blue trousers
6 a pink T-shirt

2 Find and circle. Write.

S	W	E	A	T	E	R	S	S	U	N	H	A	T	M
E	T	A	S	H	O	E	S	N	S	K	I	R	T	R
S	T	R	O	U	S	E	R	S	A	R	E	S	I	A
J	S	E	R	S	W	I	M	S	U	I	T	A	D	E

1 <u>sun</u> <u>hat</u>   2 _____   3 _____
4 _____   5 _____   6 _____

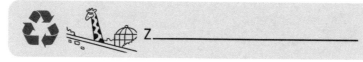

80 eighty

Lesson 2 **Grammar** 8

1 Read, follow and write.

trainers   trousers   ~~skirt~~   sun hat   T-shirt   shirt

1 I'm wearing a _____skirt_____
   and a _____.

2 I'm wearing a _____
   and _____.

3 I'm wearing a _____ _____
   and _____.

2 Draw and write. Ask and answer. Talk Partners

1 What's the weather like today?

   It's _____.

2 What are you wearing today?

   I'm wearing _____
   and _____.

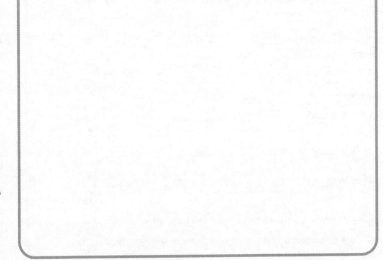

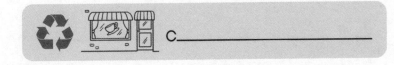

C_____

eighty-one 81

8 Lesson 3 Story

After you read

1 Remember the story. Read and circle *true* or *false*.

1 There are lots of activities at the camp. (true) false

2 The children swim in the lake. true false

3 The children ride a horse. true false

4 There's a flag at the lake. true false

5 The children sail the magic bike. true false

2 Read and write. Colour the flags.

can   can't

You _____ go in the water today. It's dangerous.

You _____ go in the water today.

  b_____

82 eighty-two

Lesson 4 **Vocabulary and Grammar** 8

1 Listen and number.

2 💬 **Talk Partners** Look at Activity 1 and write. Point, ask and answer.

sailing a boat   riding a horse   singing songs
playing volleyball   playing the guitar

1 She's _____riding a horse_____.
2 He's _____ with Molly.
3 She's _____ with her dad.
4 _____.
5 _____.

What's Molly doing?

She's riding a horse.

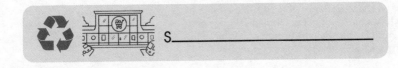 S_____

eighty-three 83

8 Lesson 5 Phonics

1 Write and say.

Toby's tongue twister

v – v – v. <u>V</u>icky the _et lo_es _olleyball.

2 Colour the words that have 'v'. Say.

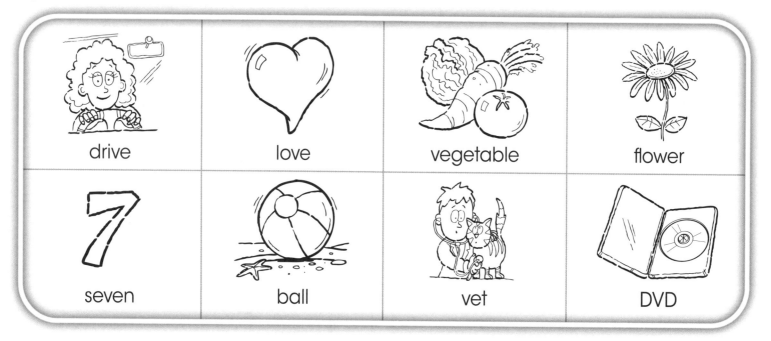

drive | love | vegetable | flower
seven | ball | vet | DVD

3 Talk Partners Play *What's my word?* in pairs.

Is it *seven*?

No, it isn't.

Is it *DVD*?

Yes, it is.

Play What's my word?: Pupils play with their Talk Partner. This is a guessing game. Pupil A chooses a word and Pupil B asks the question *Is it...?* When Pupil B guesses correctly, they swap roles and repeat.

r_____

84 eighty-four

Lesson 6 **British culture**

1 Listen and number. Write. CD4 03

sleep   stories   tent   sing   tell

We _____ songs.

We _____ scary _____.

We _____ in a _____.

💡 **Think about your culture**

What do you do in the summer?

2 Read and tick (✓). Draw, write and say.

1 I go camping.

2 I play in the sea.

3 I play volleyball.

4 I go to the forest.

5 I swim in the lake.

I _____.

♻ s_____ _____

eighty-five **85**

8 Lesson 7 Literacy

After you read

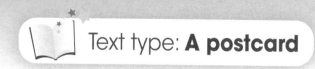
Text type: **A postcard**

1 Read again. Write *yes* or *no*.

1 Sue likes the camp.   _yes_

2 The camp is next to a river.   _____

3 Sue rides a horse at the camp.   _____

4 The weather is good.   _____

5 Sally lives in Summertown.   _____

2 Read, choose and write.

Dear _____,

I'm at a _____ camp.   beautiful   fantastic

There's a lake and there's

a _____.   forest   mountain   farm

We can do lots of activities.

I _____ and   ride a horse   swim   sing songs

I _____ every day.   play the guitar   sail a boat

The weather is _____,   hot   cold   sunny   rainy

so today I'm wearing my new _____.   swimsuit   coat

See you soon,

_____

S_____ _____

86 eighty-six

Lesson 8 Review

1 Look and write. Circle *true* or *false* for you.

1 I'm wearing ___shorts___ . true   false

2 I'm wearing a _____ . true   false

3 I'm wearing _____ . true   false

4 I'm _____ a _____ . true   false

2 Look and write.

~~painting a picture~~   playing the guitar   camp   lake
sailing a boat   ~~camp~~

  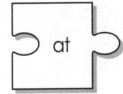 

1 She's painting a picture at the camp _____ .

  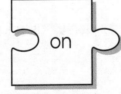 

2 He's _____ .

  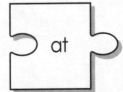 

3 _____ .

3 **My progress** Use your traffic light. Listen to the teacher and point.

Key for Activity 3: **1.** I can say different clothes. **2.** I can say what I'm wearing. **3.** I can say camp activities. **4.** I can say what somebody is doing. **5.** I can read and write a postcard. **6.** I work well with my Talk Partner.

h_____

eighty-seven 87

8 Video and 21st Century Skills

Making choices

1 What do the children choose? Listen and tick (✓).

1

2

3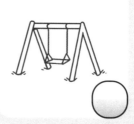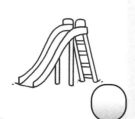

4

  What's the weather like today?

2 Think and write. Draw and say.

1 Let's go to the _____.

2 Let's wear _____.

3 Let's eat _____.

 t_____

88 eighty-eight

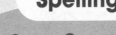

Spelling 8

Learning to learn

Let's practise spelling!

	Look		Copy	Cover and write
1		shirt	_____	_____
2		skirt	_____	_____
3		sweater	_____	_____
4		shorts	_____	_____
5		shoes	_____	_____
6		T-shirt	_____	_____
7		swimsuit	_____	_____
8		trainers	_____	_____
9		sun hat	_____ _____	_____ _____
10		trousers	_____	_____

c_____

eighty-nine 89

Lesson 1 **Vocabulary**

1 Look, read and match.

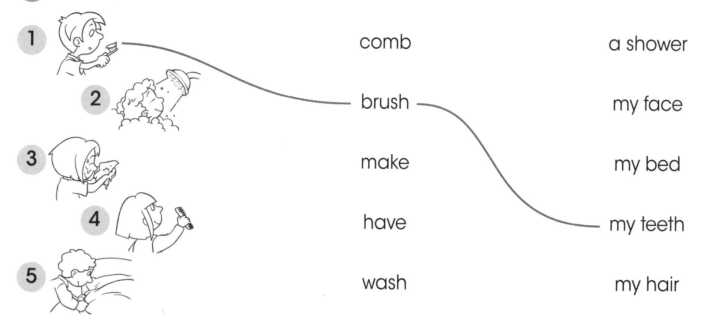

	comb	a shower
	brush	my face
	make	my bed
	have	my teeth
	wash	my hair

2 Look, read and write.

hair   shower   dressed   bed   ~~sleep~~   get   school

1 [image]
2 have a [image]
3 [image] up
4 go to [image]

5 get [image]
6 go to [image]
7 comb my [image]

Across 1: s l e e p

s_____

90 ninety

Lesson 2 **Grammar** 9

1 Read and tick (✓) or cross (✗).

1 I brush my teeth every day. ◯
2 I go to school every day. ◯
3 I sleep every day. ◯
4 I make my bed every day. ◯
5 I comb my hair every day. ◯

Monday
Tuesday
Wednesday
Thursday
Friday
Saturday
Sunday

2 Order and write.

1 every day / get up / I
   I get up every day_____.

2 go to bed / I / every day
   _____.

3 get dressed / every day / I
   _____.

4 every day / I / wash my face
   _____.

5 have a shower / every day / I
   _____.

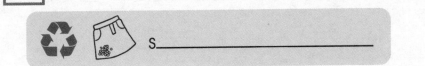
S_____

ninety-one 91

9 Lesson 3 **Story**

After you read

1 Remember the story. Read and number.

The children look for Jake's tooth. ◯

The children have dinner. ◯

The children have breakfast. ①

Jake's tooth is under his pillow. ◯

The children play in the garden. ◯

2 💬 **Talk Partners** Ask and answer. Write the names of your classmates.

Have you got a wobbly tooth?

Yes, I have.

No, I haven't.

In my class,

_____

_____

_____

_____

_____

have got a wobbly tooth.

S_____

92 ninety-two

Lesson 4 **Vocabulary and Grammar**   9

1 Listen and circle.

1
in the morning
in the afternoon

2
in the afternoon
in the evening

3
in the morning
in the evening

4
in the morning
at night

2 Read and write. Say.

My day

1 I get up _in the morning_____.

2 I have lunch _____.

3 I have a snack _____.

4 I brush my teeth _____
 and _____.

5 I play _____.

T-_____

ninety-three 93

9 Lesson 5 Phonics

1 Write and say.

Toby's tongue twister

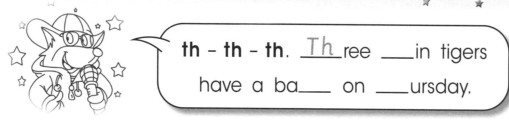

th – th – th. _Th_ree ___in tigers have a ba___ on ___ursday.

2 Colour the words that have 'th'. Say.

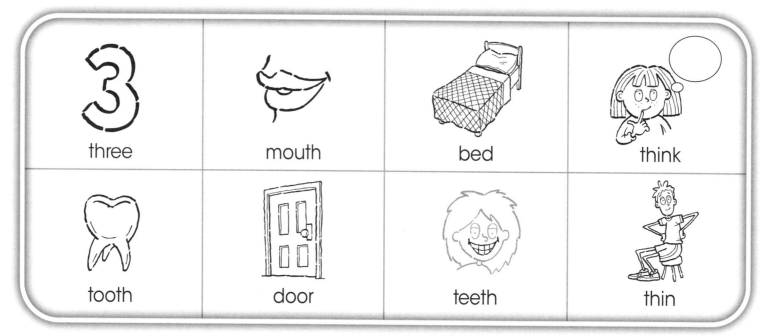

three · mouth · bed · think
tooth · door · teeth · thin

3 Talk Partners Play *Fast finger!* in pairs.

Bath!

Here!

Play Fast finger!: Pupils play with their Talk Partner. Pupil A says a word and Pupil B points to the picture as quickly as possible. They swap roles and repeat. They continue playing until they have found all the words.

S_____

94 ninety-four

Lesson 6 **British culture**

1 Read and write.

pillow   brush   ~~tooth~~   Fairy   lunch

Dear Lucy,

Thank you for your __tooth__.

There's a surprise for you under your _____.

Don't forget to _____ your teeth after breakfast, _____ and dinner.

From,

The Tooth _____ xxx

 Think about your culture

 What do you do with your tooth?

2 Read and tick (✓). Draw, write and say.

1 I put my tooth under my pillow.   ◯

2 I put my tooth in the bin.   ◯

3 I put my tooth outside.   ◯

4 I put my tooth in water.   ◯

I put my tooth _____ _____.

 t_____

9 Lesson 7 Literacy

After you read

Text type: **A poem**

1 Read and write.

owl   cockerel   ~~moon~~   sun   children   stars

1. At night, I can see the 🌙 __moon__. I can see ✨ _____.
   And I can hear an 🦉 _____.

2. In the day, I can see the ☀️ _____. I can see 👧👦 _____.
   And I can hear a 🐓 _____.

2 What do the animals say? Listen and write. 💿 CD4 23

baa   ~~cock-a-doodle-doo~~   moo   whoo whoo   woof   meow

1. cock-a-doodle-doo
2. _____
3. _____
4. _____
5. _____
6. _____

♻️ 👟 s_____

96 ninety-six

Lesson 8 Review 9

1 Number the activities for you. Write.

get dressed   ~~get up~~   have breakfast
wash my face   brush my teeth   go to school

1 I _____get up_____.
2 I _____.
3 I _____.
4 I _____.
5 I _____.
6 I _____.

2 Match and write.

| 1 breakfast | 2 lunch | 3 dinner | 4 sleep |

| night | evening | afternoon | morning |

1 I __have breakfast__ in the __morning__.
2 I _____ in the _____.
3 I _____ in the _____.
4 I _____ at _____.

3 **My progress** Use your traffic light. Listen to the teacher and point.

Key for Activity 3: 1. I can say some activities I do every day. 2. I can say the three meals of the day. 3. I can say the times of the day. 4. I can read a poem. 5. I work well with my Talk Partner.

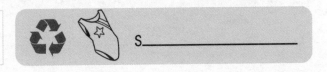

ninety-seven 97

9 Video and 21st Century Skills

Looking after your teeth

1 When do the children brush their teeth? Listen and tick (✓). CD4 26

	☀️ in the morning	⚪ in the afternoon	🌅 in the evening	🌙 at night
1 Jack	✓			
2 Bethany				
3 Anna				
4 Paul				

Do you look after your teeth? What do you do?

2 Read, think and write. Draw and say.

1 I drink _____.

2 I eat _____.

3 I brush my teeth _____ _____.

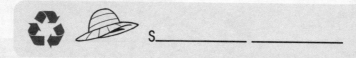

s_____ _____

98 ninety-eight

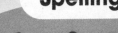

Spelling 9

Learning to learn

Let's practise spelling!

	Look	Copy	Cover and write
1	get up	_____	_____
2	wash my face	_____	_____
3	brush my teeth	_____	_____
4	comb my hair	_____	_____
5	have a shower	_____	_____
6	get dressed	_____	_____
7	go to school	_____	_____
8	make my bed	_____	_____
9	go to bed	_____	_____
10	sleep	_____	_____

t_____

ninety-nine

My project 3 Lesson 1

Plan your project

Plan your holiday list. Read, tick (✓) and write.

1 Where do you go on holiday?

the beach ◯   the mountains ◯   the city ◯

2 What's the weather like there?

sunny ◯   hot ◯

rainy ◯   cold ◯

Other: _____

3 What clothes do you wear?

a swimsuit ◯   shorts ◯

boots ◯   a sun hat ◯

Other: _____

4 What things do you use?

sunglasses ◯   map ◯

torch ◯   ball ◯

Other: _____

100 one hundred

My project 3 Lesson 2

 1 Write about your holiday.

1 I go to the _____ on holiday.

2 The weather is _____.

3 I wear _____ and _____.

4 I use _____ and _____.

Think about your project

 2 Read, think and colour the stars.

I listen to my friends.

I share my things.

I help my friends.

I make an effort.

I like the list.

one hundred and one 101

1 Vocabulary practice

1 Trace the classroom objects. Match.

1 pencil
2 pencil sharpener
3 crayon
4 rubber
5 pen
6 ruler

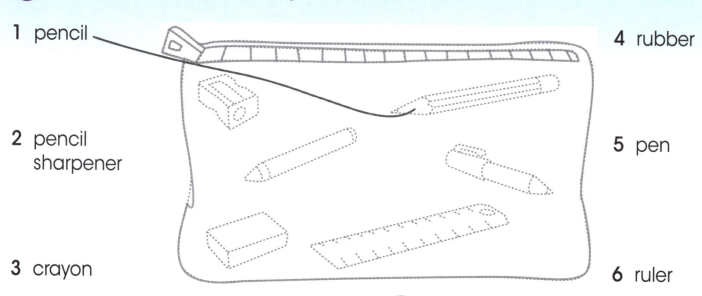

2 Find, colour and trace.

Where's my pencil?

1 book
2 computer
3 shelf
4 cupboard
5 bin
6 desk
7 board
8 chair
9 school bag

c	i	m	k	b	o	o	k	d
c	o	m	p	u	t	e	r	r
q	s	h	e	l	f	w	s	u
c	u	p	b	o	a	r	d	b
y	p	h	e	j	b	i	n	x
g	a	b	d	e	s	k	t	l
v	d	f	i	b	o	a	r	d
a	c	n	z	c	h	a	i	r
s	c	h	o	o	l	b	a	g

102 one hundred and two

Vocabulary practice 2

1 Draw the toys. Trace.

1 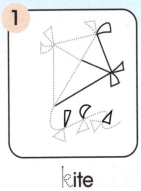 kite

2  train

3  teddy

4  car

5 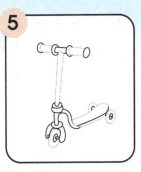 scooter

6  computer game

7 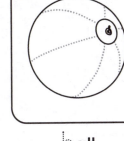 ball

8  dinosaur

9 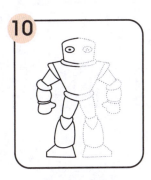 doll

10 robot

2 Read and tick (✓) or cross (✗).

 1 It's fast. ✓

 2 It's old. ○

 3 It's new. ○

 4 It's big. ○

 5 It's small. ○

 6 It's slow. ○

one hundred and three 103

3 Vocabulary practice

1 Complete the pattern. Draw.

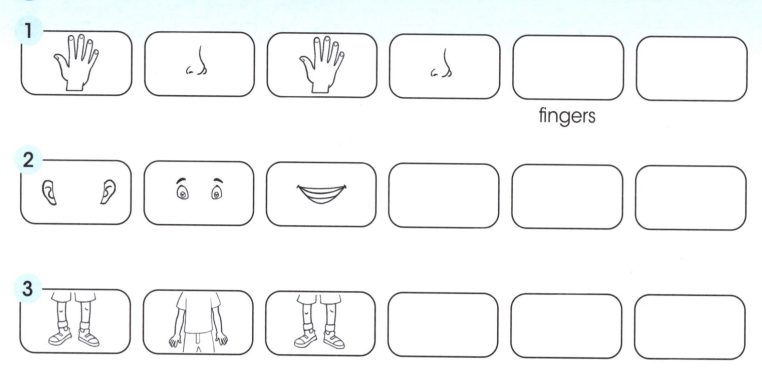

2 Look at the hair. Trace the letters in the puzzle.

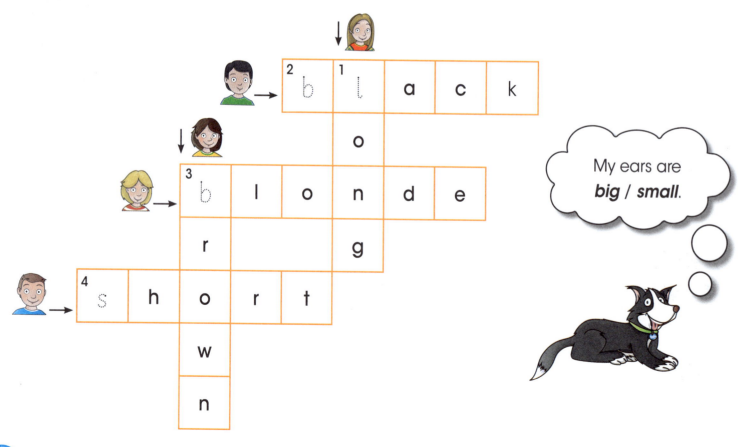

Vocabulary practice 4

1 Circle the food on the menu.

2 Look at the menu. Draw the food you like.

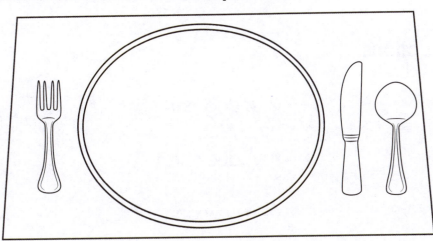

one hundred and five 105

5 Vocabulary practice

1 Find and colour the animals. Trace.

1 sheep
2 frog
3 bird
4 cat
5 mouse
6 duck

2 Look and circle.

1 frog / mouse   2 bird / chicken   3 sheep / goat

4 cow / sheep   5 cow / horse   6 goat / duck

3 Trace the actions.

1 A bird can fly.   2 A dog can run.
3 A cat can climb.   4 A duck can swim.
5 A rabbit can jump.   6 A cow can walk.

Dogs can't *jump / fly*.

106 one hundred and six

Vocabulary practice 6

1 Trace the objects in the playground. Find Toby's favourite object.

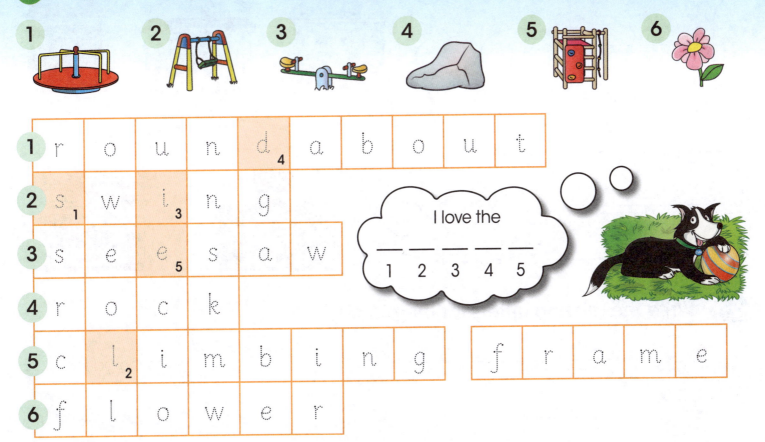

I love the _ _ _ _ _
       1 2 3 4 5

1 r o u n d a b o u t
2 s w i n g
3 s e e s a w
4 r o c k
5 c l i m b i n g   f r a m e
6 f l o w e r

2 Where's Toby? Write.

1 (near) / on the bush

2 on / in the grass

3 near / in the flowers

4 next to / in front of the tree

5 in front of / near the climbing frame

one hundred and seven 107

7 Vocabulary practice

1 Follow and write the places.

1 _____zoo_____
2 _____
3 _____
4 _____
5 _____

2 Write the missing letters for the places.

1  h o s p i t a l
2 s _ _ _ r m _ _ k _ t
3 r _ _ t _ _ r _ _ _ .
4 b _ _ k _ _ _ _ p
5 s _ _ _ m _ _ _ p _ _ l

I go to the park on my _____.

3 Match. Write the transport.

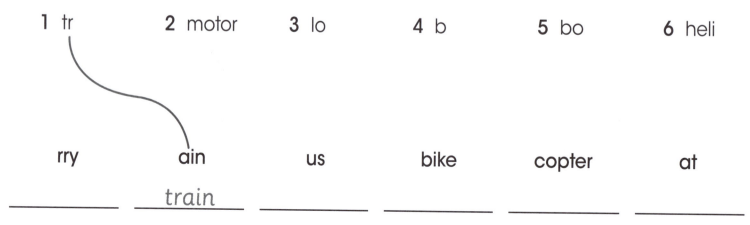

1 tr   2 motor   3 lo   4 b   5 bo   6 heli

rry   ain   us   bike   copter   at

_____ train _____ _____ _____ _____

108 one hundred and eight

Vocabulary practice 8

1 Complete the pattern. Draw and write.

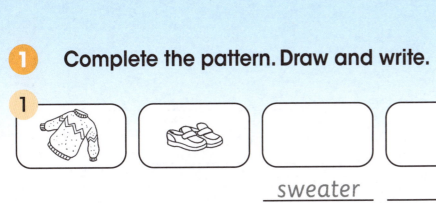

sweater

2 Write the activities. Tick (✓) the activities you like.

ride

a horse   a boat

I'm riding a _____.

one hundred and nine 109

9 Vocabulary practice

1 Match. Write the action.

1 get	to bed	_____
2 comb	up	_get up_
3 go	my face	_____
4 get	my bed	_____
5 wash	my hair	_____
6 make	dressed	_____

2 Write the sentences.

1 I _brush my teeth_ in the 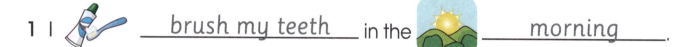 _morning_.

2 I _____ in the  _____.

3 I _____ in the _____.

4 I _____ at _____.

3 What actions do you do? Write.

In the morning	In the afternoon	In the evening	At night
get up			

It's time to go to _____.

110 one hundred and ten

1 Cambridge Exams Practice: Pre A1 Starters

Reading and Writing

1 Look and read. Write *yes* or *no*.

1 The computer is on the desk. __yes__   2 The ruler is on the board. _____

3 The pencil is under the chair. _____   4 The book is in the cupboard. _____

2 Look at the pictures. Look at the letters. Write the words.

1    p e n   e n p

2    _ _ _ _   k o b o

3    _ _ _ _ _   r e l u r

4   _ _ _ _ _ _   p i n c l e

5   _ _ _ _ _ _   b e r b u r

6  _ _ _ _ _ _ _ _ t e p c o m u r

Key learning outcome: practice for Reading and Writing Parts 2 and 3

one hundred and eleven **111**

2 Cambridge Exams Practice: Pre A1 Starters

1 Look and read. Put a tick (✓) or a cross (✗) in the box.

1  It's a car.   2 It's a chair.

3 It's a book.   4 It's a bike.

5 It's a doll.   6 It's a rubber.

2 Read this. Choose a word from the box. Write the correct word next to numbers 1–5.

My favourite toy

My favourite toy is a **1** ___ball___. It's black and

2 _____. I play with the ball at **3** _____.

I play with my **4** _____. Now the ball is in my

5 _____.

ball   school   chair   dog   white   bag   friend

Key learning outcome: practice for Reading and Writing Parts 1 and 4

3 Cambridge Exams Practice: Pre A1 Starters

1 Read this. Choose a word from the box. Write the correct word next to numbers 1–5.

My dog

My dog is **1** __brown__. It's got a black **2** _____. It's got two long **3** _____.

It's got four **4** _____. My dog's favourite toy is a **5** _____.

brown   legs   ball   cat   ears   nose   eyes

2 Look and read. Put a tick (✓) or a cross (✗) in the box.

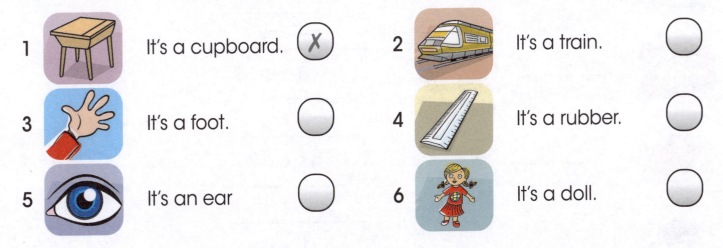

1 It's a cupboard. ✗   2 It's a train. ◯

3 It's a foot. ◯   4 It's a rubber. ◯

5 It's an ear. ◯   6 It's a doll. ◯

Key learning outcome: practice for Reading and Writing Parts 4 and 1

one hundred and thirteen

4 Cambridge Exams Practice: Pre A1 Starters

1 Look and read. Write *yes* or *no*.

1 I've got three lemons in my basket. __no__

2 I've got six eggs in my basket. _____

3 I've got two coconuts in my basket. _____

4 I've got eight bananas in my basket. _____

5 I've got four apples in my basket. _____

2 Look at the pictures. Look at the letters. Write the words.

1   e g g — g e g

2   _ _ _ _ — s h i f

3   _ _ _ _ — k e a c

4   _ _ _ _ _ — n o l e m

5   _ _ _ _ _ _ _ — i c h n e c k

6   _ _ _ _ _ _ _ — n o t u c o c

Key learning outcome: practice for Reading and Writing Parts 2 and 3

5 Cambridge Exams Practice: Pre A1 Starters

1 Look and read. Put a tick (✓) or a cross (✗) in the box.

1  This is a cow. ✓   2 This is a doll. ◯

3 This is a sheep. ◯   4 This is an ear. ◯

5 This is a ruler. ◯   6 This is a grape. ◯

2 Look and read. Write *yes* or *no*.

1 The cat is black. ___no___   2 The horse has got an apple. _____

3 The girl has got short hair. _____   4 The duck can swim. _____

5 The dog has got a long tail. _____

Key learning outcome: practice for Reading and Writing Parts 1 and 2

one hundred and fifteen

6 Cambridge Exams Practice: Pre A1 Starters

1 Look at the picture and read the questions. Write one-word answers.

1 Where is the girl?   next to the ___*flowers*___

2 Where are the birds?   _____ the tree

3 What toy has the boy got?   a _____

4 What is in front of the tree? a _____

5 What colour is the boy's hair? _____

2 Look and read. Put a tick (✓) or a cross (✗) in the box.

 1 This is a flower. ✓   2 This is a frog.

 3 This is a tree.   4 This is a peach.

 5 This is a chair.   6 This is an eye.

116 one hundred and sixteen

Key learning outcome: practice for Reading and Writing Parts 5 and 1

7 Cambridge Exams Practice: Pre A1 Starters

1 Look at the pictures. Look at the letters. Write the words.

1 b u s   s u b

2   _ _ _ _   t a b o

3 _ _ _ _ _   t a r i n

4   _ _ _ _ _   r o y r l

5   _ _ _ _ _ _ _ _ _   e k i b t o r o m

2 Read this. Choose a word from the box. Write the correct word next to numbers 1–5.

The zoo

There is a zoo in my **1** ___town___. I go to the zoo

by **2** _____. There are a lot of animals. I can

see **3** _____ in the water and I can see

4 _____ in the trees. I can play in a

5 _____ too. The zoo is fantastic!

town   car   flowers   dogs   juice   birds   playground   fish

Key learning outcome: practice for Reading and Writing Parts 3 and 4

one hundred and seventeen 117

8 Cambridge Exams Practice: Pre A1 Starters

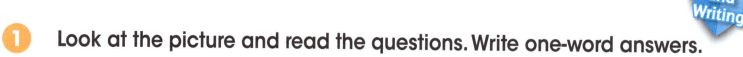

1 Look at the picture and read the questions. Write one-word answers.

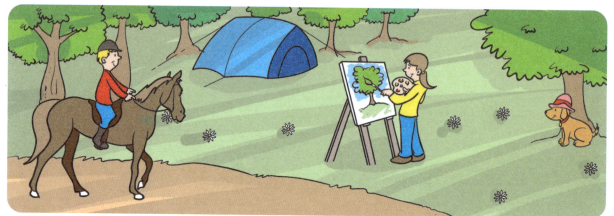

1 What is the dog wearing? a _____hat_____

2 What is the boy doing? riding a _____

3 What is the girl doing? _____ a picture

4 Where is the dog? in front of a _____

5 How many flowers are there? _____

2 Look at the pictures. Look at the letters. Write the words.

1 k o s c 2 h e o s 3 k i s t r 4 t h i r s 5 T-h i s t r 6 r e s t s o u r

1 s o c k   2 _ _ _ _ _

3 _ _ _ _ _ _   4 _ _ _ _ _

5 _ _ _ _ _ _ _   6 _ _ _ _ _ _ _

118 one hundred and eighteen

Key learning outcome: practice for Reading and Writing Parts 5 and 3

9 Cambridge Exams Practice: Pre A1 Starters

Reading and Writing

1 Read this. Choose a word from the box. Write the correct word next to numbers 1–5.

My day

In the morning, I have a big <u>breakfast</u>.

At school, I read a **1** _____ and I listen

to the **2** _____. In the afternoon, I have

3 _____ and I **4** _____ with my friends.

At **5** _____, I sleep.

breakfast   lunch   computer   book   teacher   play   night

2 Look and read. Write *yes* or *no*.

1 The boy has got black hair.   <u>yes</u>

2 There are five apples on the cupboard. _____

3 The girl is drinking water. _____

4 The bags are under the table. _____

5 The boy is eating bread. _____

Key learning outcome: practice for Reading and Writing Parts 4 and 2

Macmillan Education Limited
4 Crinan Street
London N1 9XW

Companies and representatives throughout the world

Give Me Five! English Level 1 Activity Book Basics
ISBN 978-1-380-01376-7
Give Me Five! English Level 1 Activity Book Basics with
Digital Activity Book ISBN 978-1-380-06594-0

Text © Donna Shaw and Joanne Ramsden 2018
Design and illustration © Macmillan Education Limited 2018

The authors have asserted their right to be identified as the authors
of this work in accordance with the Copyright, Designs and Patents
Act 1988.

This edition published 2020
First edition entitled *High Five! English* published 2014 by Macmillan
Education Limited

All rights reserved. No part of this publication may be reproduced,
stored in a retrieval system, or transmitted in any form or by
any means, electronic, mechanical, photocopying, recording, or
otherwise, without the prior written permission of the publishers.

Series concept design by Tom Cole
Designed by Anthony Godber
Page makeup by Anthony Godber and emc design ltd

Illustrated by Kathy Baxendale, Sam Church, Nigel Dobbyn, Clive
Goodyer, Andy Keylock, Dusan Pavlic, Julia Patton, Ángeles
Peinador, Andy Robb, Tony De Saulles, Jorge Santillán, Eric Smith,
Simon Smith, Sholto Walker and Matt Ward.

Cover design by Bigtop Design Limited
Cover photographs by **Getty Images**/iStockphoto/Thinkstock
Images/katsto80; Tom Dick and Debbie Productions
Cover illustration by Ángeles Peinador
Course consultants: Rocío Gutiérrez Burgos and Mónica Pérez Is
Recordings produced by Footsteps and Tom Dick and Debbie
Productions
Picture research by Sally Cole and Fernanda Rocha / Ikonia LLC

Authors' acknowledgements
The authors would like to thank everyone at Macmillan who has
given help and advice throughout this project. Special thanks from
Jo to Carlos, Daniel and Alex for their patience and support during
this process. Special thanks from Donna to José, Elisa, Teresa and
Marina for their encouragement and enthusiasm.

Printed and bound in Uruguay

2022
31

Acknowledgments
The publishers would like to thank the following teachers for their
contribution to the project:
Amanda Morrison Prince, Colegio El Parque, La Navata, Madrid;
Amaya Carrera García, Colegio Santa Teresa de Jesús, Valladolid;
Ana Fernández Sáez, CEIP La Encina, Las Rozas, Madrid; Aránzazu
Sánchez Rodríguez, CEIP Rosa Luxemburgo, Madrid; Beatriz
García Vaquero, CEIP Mariano José de Larra, Madrid; Carme
Tena, Col·legi Sagrada Familia, Tortosa, Tarragona; Cristina Nieto
Ruíz de Gaona, CEIP Margarita Salas, Arroyo de la Encomienda,
Valladolid; Estíbaliz Medina Martín, CEIP Virgen de Navalazarza, San
Agustín de Guadalix, Madrid; Iratxe Zabaleta Zendagorta, Ikastola
San Fidel, Guernica, Vizcaya; Lucía Soria García, CEIP Alberto
Alcocer, Madrid; M.ª Carmen Lago Muñoz, CEIP Federico García
Lorca, Colmenar Viejo, Madrid; Marta Moreno Arroyo, CEIP Vicente
Aleixandre, Móstoles, Madrid; Susana Espinel Beneitez, Colegio
Grazalema, El Puerto de Santa María, Cádiz; Susana García Pizarro,
Ateneu Instructiu, Sant Joan Despi, Barcelona; Virginia Escalona
Monreal, CEIP La Encina, Las Rozas, Madrid; Mónica Pérez Is, CEIP
Reina Victoria, Madrid; Rocío Gutierrez, CEIP Lepanto, Madrid;
Laura Zarzuelo, Colegio Virgen de la Almudena, Collado Villalba,
Madrid; Eugenio Domínguez, Colegio Virgen de la Almudena,
Collado Villalba, Madrid; Silvia Díez de Rivera, Colegio Orvalle, Las
Rozas, Madrid; Maite Crespo, Colegio Jesús Nazareno, Madrid;
Silvia Valderrama, CEIP Benito Pérez Galdós, Arganda del Rey,
Madrid; Cristina Baeza, CEIP Rosa Chacel, Collado Villalba, Madrid;
Leyre Alcalde; CEIP Cortes de Cádiz, Madrid; María Andrés, Colegio
Matter Inmaculata, Madrid.

The authors and publishers would like to thank the following for
permission to reproduce their photographs:
Alamy Stock Photo/Ian Fraser p.75 (top); Fancy p.53 (top); **Getty
Images**/E+/vpopovic pp111–119 (top banner), Getty Images/The
Image Bank/Paul Taylor p.85 (top); **Macmillan Publishers Ltd.**/
Lisa Payne pp.11, 21, 31, 43, 53, 63, 75, 85, 95; **Plainpictur**e/
Helge Sauber p63 (top), Plainpicture/OJO/Robert Daly p.43(top);
Shutterstock/JPC-PROD p.21 (top banner); Shutterstock/
LeksusTuss p.31 (top banner).

Commissioned photography by Lisa Payne (pp.11, 21, 31, 43, 53,
63, 75, 85, 95) and Tom Dick and Debbie Productions (pp.14, 24,
34, 46, 56, 66, 78, 88, 98).

These materials may contain links for third party websites. We have
no control over, and are not responsible for, the contents of such
third party websites. Please use care when accessing them.

The inclusion of any specific companies, commercial products,
trade names or otherwise, does not constitute or imply its
endorsement or recommendation by Macmillan Education Limited.